UNIT 16 • Wild, Wild West

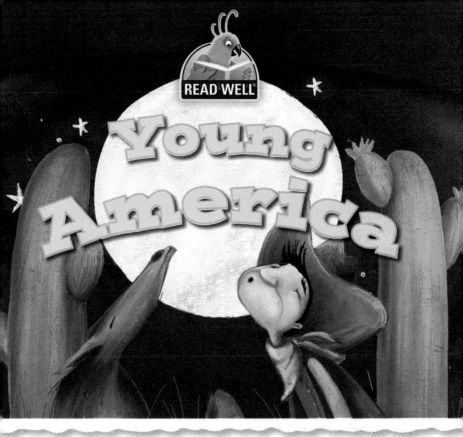

UNITS 15, 16

5 6 7 8 9   RRD   14 13 12 11 10

Read Well is a registered trademark of Sopris West Educational Services.

IISBN 978-1-60218-555-5
ISBN 1-60218-555-7

Printed in the United States of America
Published and Distributed by

Cambium
LEARNING®
Sopris West®

4093 Specialty Place • Longmont, CO 80504 • (303) 651-2829
www.sopriswest.com

167290/1-10

UNIT 15

Snapshots of the American West

Introduction, Chapters 1, 2

Vocabulary

★ **the West**

If you look at a map of the United States, the land on the left side of the Mississippi River is called **the West**.

My family is planning to drive from the Bronx to *the West*. What river will we have to cross? Point to the map and show me the area that my family may visit.

★ **pi·o·neer**

A **pioneer** is one of the first people to travel to a new place.

The first people to travel to the West in covered wagons were called *pioneers*. Why were they called pioneers?

★ **tribe**

A **tribe** is a group of people who live in an area together. Members of a tribe share the same customs, language, and beliefs.

An American Indian is a member of a . . .

★ = New

★ A·rap·a·ho

Arapaho is the name of an American Indian tribe.

The *Arapaho* people live in the area now known as the states of Colorado, Wyoming, and Oklahoma. Name a tribe that lives in Colorado.

★ scout

On a hunt or expedition, a **scout** will leave the group to go see what is ahead.

When Jack and his friends went exploring, Jack was the *scout*. What was Jack's job?

★ leg·gings

Leggings are clothes that cover just your legs or part of your legs.

Dancers often wear *leggings* to keep their legs warm. Point to the leggings in the picture.

Introduction

Two hundred years ago, the West was a place where American Indian tribes lived as they had for hundreds of years. It was a place where pioneers traveled many miles to make new homes. What do you know about the American West in the 1800s?

Here are stories and photographs about the Old West—Indians, buffalo, pioneers, settlers, and the building of the railroads. Imagine that you lived in the Old West. What would your life have been like? Would you have hunted buffalo? Would your family have traveled west in a covered wagon? Would you have settled in a new home out West? Perhaps you would have helped build the railroads.

Chapter 1

Buffalo Hunt

South Platte River, 1835

1800   1835   1900

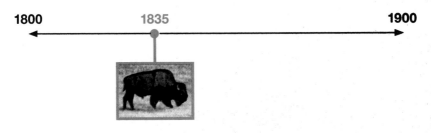

"Ho, Many Falls!"

"Ho, Dark Cloud!"

The two boys looked at each other from their horses. They wore strong buffalo-hide moccasins. Deerskin leggings covered their legs. A long piece of deerskin was folded under each boy's belt in front and back. Each boy carried a long bow made of cedar and buffalo muscle. A pouch tied to their belts held a hunting knife and a bundle of arrows.

This was a special day for Many Falls and Dark Cloud. Each boy was eleven years old. Today, they would go on their first buffalo hunt.

___

Describe the main characters. Was it an *ordinary* day? Why not?

Like all Arapaho boys, Many Falls and Dark Cloud had learned to ride horses when they were very young. When Many Falls was only five, his father put him on a pony. He slipped off the pony's back and fell. Each time the boy fell, he tried again. This happened many times. The boy was given the name Many Falls. His uncle said, "Many Falls is very brave. When he falls, he is ready to try again."

Over time, Many Falls learned to ride well. He held onto the pony with his knees and used his legs and feet to tell his pony what to do. His hands were free to shoot his bow.

On the day of the big hunt, Many Falls and Dark Cloud followed the other hunters. The scouts saw a herd of buffalo. They led the men to the buffalo. The men would hunt for one buffalo, but only one.

What *tribe* did the boys belong to? Do you think Many Falls' uncle is *impressed* with him? Why?

The hunters yelled and rode fast. The buffalo herd started running. The lead hunter was Red Knife. He rode his horse right beside the herd. He drove one buffalo away from the rest. It came straight at Many Falls!

Many Falls turned his horse and shot an arrow. The other men rode hard and fired arrows. When the hunt was done, Many Falls' uncle spoke to him.

"That was a swift arrow you shot," he said. "Tonight, we will tell the story of the hunt. From today, your name will be Swift Arrow." Swift Arrow was proud and very happy.

What was Many Falls' new name? How did he earn his new name?

Think and Talk

DRAWING CONCLUSIONS

1. How did the boy get the name Many Falls?

INFERENCE, EXPLANATION

2. Explain how Many Falls was able to shoot an arrow while riding a horse.

DRAWING CONCLUSIONS

3. Why do you think the men hunted for only one buffalo?

INFERENCE

4. Why did Many Falls' name get changed to Swift Arrow? Why was he happy and proud?

Chapter 2

The Mighty Buffalo

Making Use of the Buffalo

For hundreds of years, the American Indians of the Great Plains hunted buffalo. They hunted only when they needed buffalo meat for food. The buffalo hides were used for tepee covers, blankets, beds, and clothing.

Using the Insides

Plains Indians used every part of the animal they could. They used small bones as knives and tools. The big buffalo stomach became a cooking pot. Gallstones made great yellow paint, and they used buffalo brains for cleaning hides—yes, buffalo brains!

Why did the Plains Indians hunt the buffalo? Look back at the last paragraph. Name four ways the American Indians used buffalo parts.

Bow

Bowstring ➜

Did the Plains Indians use buffalo muscles? Yes, they dried buffalo muscles into bowstrings. They needed bowstrings on their bows so they could shoot their arrows while hunting. Indians also dried the muscles into sewing thread for making clothes.

Using the Outside

What did they do with the hooves? Made glue! Did they use buffalo hair? Yes, they used the hair for rope and bed stuffing. What did they do with the horns? They drank from them. Last but not least, what about the buffalo's tail? Indians used buffalo tails in the same way the buffalo did—to shoo away pesky flies.

Horn

Tail

Name six more ways the Plains Indians used the buffalo. Explain why the buffalo was so important to the Plains Indians.

Chapter 3

Vocabulary

★ com·mu·ni·cate

Communicate means to share ideas or feelings with someone else. You can communicate by talking, writing, making faces, or using your hands.

If someone waves at you, what is that person *communicating*? Without talking, communicate to me that you're happy.

★ trade

If I give you something and you give me something in return, we **trade**.

José and Trevor liked to *trade* baseball cards. What do you like to trade?

★ trad·er

Someone who trades with another person is called a **trader**.

When Trevor is older, he hopes to go to a meeting with other people who trade cards. Trevor and the others will be card . . .

★ dis·tance

Distance is the amount of space between things. A distance can be very small or very large.

When my friend lived next door, there was very little *distance* between our houses. Now that she lives across the country, there is a long distance between us. With your hands, show me the distance between your two shoulders.

★ = New

Chapter 3

Talking Without Words

More than 500 American Indian tribes live in North America today. At one time, the tribes spoke different languages (many still do), but they wanted to trade things with each other. This meant that they needed to talk with one another. They needed to communicate.

Talking With Sign Language

People from one tribe traded with others. One tribe might have warm buffalo robes and blankets. Another tribe might have a hard rock called flint. Flint is good for making knives, arrowheads, and other tools.

A trader with flint knives would meet another trader who had buffalo robes. The trader would put three knives on the ground. The other would shake his head "no." Three knives for a buffalo robe may not have been fair.

The first trader would try again. He would put down another knife. Then the second trader might have nodded "yes." Four knives for one robe may have been a good trade.

Nodding your head for "yes" or "no" is an example of sign language. You could also use your hands to sign. American Indians from many places learned to communicate in this way. They could talk about many things even though they did not speak the same language.

Why did the tribes *trade* with each other? Why couldn't people from different tribes talk with one another? Why was sign language important to American Indians?

Talking With Pictures

Another way to speak is with pictures. Some American Indians painted pictures on rocks. These are called pictographs. Some pictographs have survived for hundreds of years. The pictographs mark places that were special to a tribe. Pictographs are a way of saying, "Our people were here."

Talking With Smoke

Some tribes used smoke signals. This allowed people to communicate over long distances. Water or wet animal hide on a fire makes a puff of smoke. The smoke signals may have shared good news about a nearby buffalo herd.

Pictograph

Smoke Signal

Name two more ways American Indians sometimes communicated without talking.

Powwows

Sometimes, thousands of American Indians from many tribes met in one place for many days. They traded dried meat, beads, clothing, tools, arrowheads, baskets, pots, and much more at these gatherings. People who knew more than one language would help others communicate.

Today, people from many tribes still meet at gatherings. These gatherings are called powwows. The people dance, sing, tell stories, and trade goods with one another.

Powwow 1800s

Powwow Today

What did American Indians trade in the past? What is a powwow?

FACT, LOCATING INFORMATION

1. Look back in your book and find the fact that tells how many American Indian tribes live in North America.

INFERENCE

2. Why did people from different tribes trade with each other?

DRAWING CONCLUSIONS

3. How can you communicate with someone who speaks a different language?

EXPLANATION

4. How were smoke signals created and what were they used for?

COMPARE

5. How are powwows today like those of long ago?

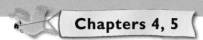

Chapters 4, 5

Vocabulary

pi·o·neer

A **pioneer** is one of the first people to travel to a new place.

The people who traveled to the West in wagon trains were called *pioneers*. If you traveled to an island where no one had ever been, what would you be called?

★ Mis·sou·ri

Missouri is one of the 50 United States.

Find *Missouri* on the map.

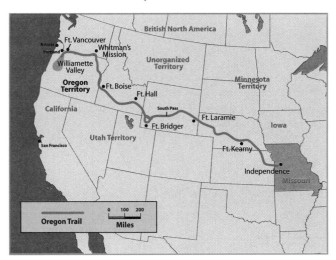

★ = New

★ wil·low branch

A **willow branch** comes from a willow tree. A willow branch is long and thin and bends easily.

We cooked our hot dogs on a *willow branch* over the campfire. Touch the willow branch in the picture.

★ scorch·er

When a day is very hot, people call it a **scorcher**.

I worked outside in the sun yesterday, and it was quite a *scorcher*. Use your new vocabulary word to tell me what kind of day it was.

Now You Try It!

Try defining each word. Then look up the word in the glossary. Your definition might be better!

ex·haust·ing

Start with "*Exhausting* means . . ." Let's find the word on page 98.

daw·dle

Start with "When you *dawdle* . . ." Let's find the word on page 96.

★ = New

Chapter 4

Life on the Trail

Missouri, 1843–1869

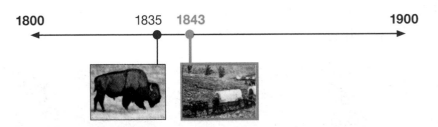

| 1800 | 1835 | 1843 | 1900 |

About 150 years ago, pioneers gathered in Missouri to start a six-month journey west. Their wagons were crammed with their belongings and treasured things. Food was packed, and excitement filled the air.

By the end of the first day, pioneers had traveled about 15 miles. They had about 2,000 miles left to go.

Each day on the trail was full of adventure and hard work. If the weather was harsh, the day was difficult. If the trail was bad, the day was exhausting. Pioneers needed to cross the mountains by winter, or they would be blocked by snow. There was no time to dawdle.

Sometimes, the wagon trains had to cross a river. If a river was deep, the pioneers would lift their wagons off the wheels and float the wagons across the river.

Each morning by 4:00 a.m., with the sky as dark as night, pioneers were up and moving. They hurried in the darkness to make breakfast, milk the cows, round up the cattle, pull down tents, and load their wagons. Phew! By 7:00 a.m., the wagon train was rolling.

Bump, bump, bumpity, bump—the road was so bumpy that milk turned into butter by the evening.

Sometimes, a sudden windstorm whipped up the sandy dirt. By the end of the day, faces were covered with dirt and sweat. Eyes were red and puffy. Still, the pioneers got up the next day and continued on, trying to get to the West, where they could make new homes.

What made the trip west difficult? Do you think you would have liked life on the trail? Why or why not?

Chapter 5

A River Crossing
South Platte River, 1850

1800   1835   1843   1850   1900

June 22, 1850

Dear Gramps:

Today was another river crossing! Pa and I made our third raft. We used wood and willow branches. Pa said I'm getting really good at tying knots. Ma and Rachel used candle wax and ashes to make a paste. The paste helps make the raft waterproof.

We all took the wheels off the wagons again. Then we put the wagons on the rafts. It was hard work. It was a scorcher, so we had sweat dripping off our brows. Ma had to watch the babies. I think she was kind of nervous about crossing the river because of what happened to the Browns.

The Browns are traveling with us now. Their wagon was dragged down the river during the last crossing! It was a pretty awful sight. The Browns lost everything except a barrel of flour. They saved the flour, but Ma says it's all wet and muddy from the river. Pa says it's lucky no one was hurt.

29

The river was calm today, so we got across this river just fine. Our oxen and horses swam to the other side. We didn't lose anything. Everything stayed tied down on the wagon. All the wagons are safe across the river. It was a good day.

Everyone says Oregon is a great place. They say there are tall trees and rivers and streams filled with fish. Pa says the land is good for farming. We reckon it will be a long time before we get there.

We miss you, Gramps. Hope this gets to you.
Love,
Andy

Chapters 6, 7

Vocabulary

im·mi·grant

A person who moves from one country to another is called an **immigrant**.

Immigrants came to the United States from many other countries. A person who is born in China and comes to live in the United States is an . . .

★ rav·e·nous

When you are **ravenous**, you are very hungry.

I was so *ravenous* after swimming that I ate four sandwiches. I ate an enormous dinner, so I must have been . . .

★ for·mer

We use the word **former** to describe what someone used to be.

Mrs. Dalton used to be a soldier. Mrs. Dalton is a . . .

★ = New

Idioms and Expressions

★ make a name for ourselves

When we **make a name for ourselves**, we do something so great that other people hear about us.

Our baseball team won so many games that we *made a name for ourselves*. If a dancer wanted to make a name for himself, what could he do?

★ hold my head up high

When **I hold my head up high**, I am proud of something I did.

I could *hold my head up high* because I did my best. What do you do that makes you hold your head up high?

Now You Try It!

Try defining the next word. Then look up the word in the glossary. Your definition might be better!

★ dan·ger·ous

Start with "When something is *dangerous* . . ."
Let's find the word on page 96.

★ = New

Chapter 6

The Great Railroad
(1863–1869)

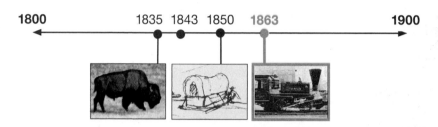

1800   1835 1843 1850   1863   1900

With people moving to the West, the U.S. government wanted to complete a railroad that went from one coast to the other. In 1863, one railroad company started in the West in California. Another started in Nebraska to the east.

Why do you think people wanted a railroad that went to the West?

Thousands of men worked together to build the railroad. The men were Chinese and Irish immigrants, former slaves, and former soldiers.

They worked to make the ground flat, and they dug tunnels through mountains. They laid down heavy wooden ties and heavy steel rails. They pounded spikes to hold the track in place. It was hard, dangerous work, and at first they earned only one dollar a day.

In Utah on May 10, 1869, the two railroads finally met. Every worker felt proud. The new railroad would change America forever. Before, when pioneers moved to the West in wagon trains, it took many months. On a train, people could travel from coast to coast in fewer than 10 days.

The railroad made Americans feel closer to each other. They could visit people in other states, send mail quickly, and buy things from far away. Many immigrants moved out of crowded cities in the East and built farms and small towns out West. Farmers and ranchers grew more food because they could ship it to market by rail.

Describe what building the railroad was like. How did the railroads change life in the United States?

Think and Talk

FACT

1. Who built the railroads?

CAUSE AND EFFECT

2. Look back at the third paragraph on page 34. How did life in the United States change?

DRAWING CONCLUSIONS

3. The book says that Americans felt closer to one another. They could visit, send mail quickly, and buy things from far away. How do you think this made Americans feel about the railroad?

PERSONAL RESPONSE

4. If you had lived in the 1800s, would you have wanted to go west with a wagon train or ride on a railroad train? Why?

DRAWING CONCLUSIONS

5. The book doesn't tell how the railroads affected the buffalo hunters. How do you think the railroads and the movement west affected the Plains Indians? How do you think they felt about the railroads?

Chapter 7

Ming Mei, Railroad Worker
California, 1869

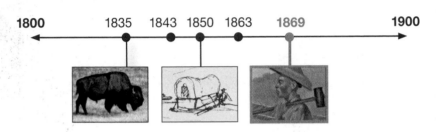

1800   1835   1843   1850   1863   1869   1900

My name is Ming Mei (May). When I was 18, I made the long trip from China to California to seek my fortune. I came to the United States because I had heard there was a mountain of gold.

I helped dig tunnels in the Sierra Nevada mountains, but I did not see a sparkle of gold. I saw only the sweat of my body. I remember the grunts of men laying track around me. The sledgehammers beside me rang as spikes were pounded into the ground.

Who is telling the story? Why did Ming Mei come to the United States? Instead of finding gold, what did Ming Mei end up doing in the United States?

There were many Chinese workers laying tracks. We worked hard. We made a fine name for ourselves in this country. As we worked, I saw miles of perfect railroad tracks behind us. I held my head up high.

The mountains were beautiful, but the air was bitter cold. We were ravenous after a hard day's work. We ate fish with soy sauce, rice, and vegetables. Our food and tea made us strong. It reminded us of our old home in China.

There were also many Irish workers. The Irish had to eat what the bosses gave them—boiled beef and potatoes every day. Nothing else. They were often sick from this food or from the water they drank.

After working on the rails, why did Ming Mei *hold his head up high*? What made the Chinese workers strong? Who else helped build the railroads? How was their food different from Ming Mei's?

One day in 1869, the railroad from the West met up with the railroad from the East. We had built an amazing thing—a railroad that reached all the way across the country.

We were part of something important. We all cheered joyously. The Irish and the Chinese cheered together. We helped build America.

Why did the Irish and the Chinese cheer together? Why were the Irish and Chinese *immigrants* proud?

39

Chapters 8, 9

Vocabulary

★ prai·rie

Prairie is flat, open land that is covered with grass.

Much of the middle part of the United States is still *prairie*. Can you think of things that you will not find on a prairie?

★ dug·out

A **dugout** is a room that is made by digging a large hole in the ground or the side of a hill.

Long ago, people sometimes had to live in a room made in the side of a hill. That room was called a . . .

★ set·tler

A **settler** is someone who moves to where few people are living and makes a home there.

Settlers moved to the West by wagon train. What's another word for people who moved to the West to build homes?

Now You Try It!

Try defining the next word. Then look up the word in the glossary. Your definition might be better!

em·bar·rassed

Start with "*Embarrassed* means to be . . . " Let's find the word on page 97.

★ = New

Chapter 8

Betsy's New Home
Nebraska, 1885

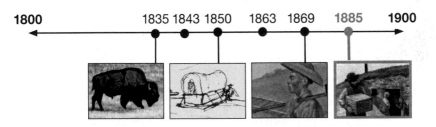

Betsy's father was waiting in the wagon. She and her big brother, Willie, jumped off the train. They raced to hug Papa. Their mother followed. A month before, Papa had moved out to the land they had paid for. "He's building our new house," Mama said.

Before long, they were on the dirt road. Betsy looked around. All she could see was land covered in grass. She did not see any buildings. And something else was missing. "Where are the trees?" Betsy asked.

Where did Betsy and her family move? How did the family travel? Why do you think they moved?

"This is the prairie," Willie answered. "There aren't many trees out here." This made Betsy sad. She liked the big trees around their farmhouse in Indiana. But now they had moved to Nebraska— 600 miles away.

Finally, Papa stopped the oxen. They were on top of a small hill. Betsy saw a creek nearby. "Here we are," Papa said.

Betsy was excited. "Where's the house?" she asked.

Papa chuckled. "You're standing on it," he said. He and Willie began unloading boxes from the wagon. They also unloaded two glass windows and a door.

How was Betsy's old home in Indiana different from her new home?

Betsy and her mother walked down the hill. There were two small windows in the side of the hill. They did not have any glass in them. Between them was a doorway without a door.

Betsy looked up at Mama. "Is that our house?" she asked.

Mama nodded and smiled. "It's called a dugout."

Betsy peeked inside. It was dark and smelled like dirt. The walls were dirt, and the floor was dirt. A small wood stove stood in the corner. In the center was their old table. They were going to live inside the hill!

Why do you think Betsy's father made a *dugout* for a home? Do you think Betsy will like living inside the hill?

Mama found a bucket. "Betsy, please fetch some water from the creek," Mama said.

When Betsy got back, Papa and Willie were already putting in the windows. Then they hung the door in the doorway. Mama had a fire going in the stove. Betsy could smell a yummy pot of pork and beans.

They sat down for dinner. A chunk of dirt fell from the ceiling. It landed in Papa's empty bowl. They all laughed. But Papa looked a little embarrassed.

"Next year, we'll build a regular house," he said, "after we get the crops planted."

"Can we plant trees too?" Betsy asked.

Papa smiled and gave her a wink. "We sure can," he said.

Think and Talk

DRAWING CONCLUSIONS

1. Betsy's father moved west before the rest of the family. Why do you think he moved first?

CONTRAST

2. Betsy used to live in Indiana before moving to Nebraska. How is Nebraska different from where she had lived in Indiana?

DESCRIPTION

3. Describe Betsy's new home in Nebraska. What kind of house was it?

GENERATING IDEAS

4. If you lived with Betsy in her new home, what might your day be like?

INFERENCE

5. Why do you think Papa was embarrassed when a chunk of dirt fell from the ceiling into his bowl?

Chapter 9

Betsy's Diary
Nebraska, 1886

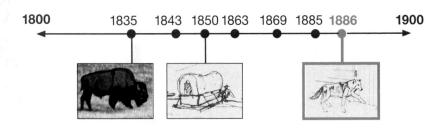

1800   1835   1843   1850 1863   1869   1885 1886   1900

What was a settler's life like in the West? There were no weather reports back then. Sometimes bad weather took people by surprise. This diary is based on real stories from the 1800s.

January 5, 1886
The weather has been nice. Papa took the wagon to town this morning. He'll stay there until tomorrow. He says he has a surprise for us.

January 6, 1886
Willie and I saw big dark clouds this afternoon. We ran back to the dugout. Then it started snowing hard. Some snow came under the door, and Mama stuffed rags there to block it. But the stove keeps us warm. Mama and I brought the chickens into the house to keep them safe.

January 7, 1886

It's snowing so hard that you can't see very far. And the snow is getting very deep outside. Willie had to go to the shed to feed and milk Irma, our cow. We tied a rope around his middle so he wouldn't get lost. When he came back, he was covered in snow. He looked like a snowman! But he had a bucket of warm milk. Mama says she's worried about Papa. I am too. I'm worried he got caught in the snowstorm.

January 9, 1886

The snow finally stopped, but it's really cold outside. We have plenty of potatoes and bacon to eat. And we still have some wood for the fire.

January 10, 1886

Last night we heard scratching at the door. At first we thought maybe it was Papa. But this morning we saw wolf tracks outside. I'm not scared. Papa says I'm brave. But I sure wish he'd come home.

January 11, 1886
We ran out of wood so we had to burn some floorboards this morning. Now I'm a little scared.

January 12, 1886
This morning we stayed in bed to keep warm. We heard thumping on the roof. I thought maybe the wolves were back. Then we heard footsteps. A big snowman appeared in the doorway. It was Papa!

January 13, 1886
I asked Papa about the surprise. He said we would get the secret when the snow melted. Then Papa whispered, "Can you keep a secret?" I nodded. Papa whispered, "It's a piano. I got your Mama and you a piano."

Chapter 10

Vocabulary

★ **Chey·enne**

Cheyenne (Shy-ann) is the name of a Great Plains Indian tribe.

In the *Cheyenne* tribe, the women took down the tepees whenever the tribe moved. In what tribe did the women take down the tepees?

★ **res·er·va·tion**

A **reservation** is an area of land that is set aside for a special purpose.

As settlers built homes in the West, the Indians living there were sent to live on *reservations*. Where were many American Indians sent to live?

for·mer

We use the word **former** to describe what someone used to be.

Freddie used to be a farmer. Freddie is a . . .

★ **home·stead**

A **homestead** is a large piece of land given to a settler to farm.

The U.S. government granted *homesteads* to people who were willing to move to the West. Many settlers started farms on their . . .

★ = New

★ re·ly

When you **rely** on someone, you trust and expect help from that person.

Some of you *rely* on the bus driver to get you to school each day. Who else do you rely on? Start with "I rely on . . ."

Now You Try It!

Try defining the next word. Then look up the word in the glossary. Your definition might be better!

com·mun·i·ty

Start with "A *community* is a . . ." Let's find the word on page 96.

be·long·ings

Start with "*Belongings* are . . ." Let's find the word on page 95.

★ = New

Chapter 10

Children in the 1800s: Photo Essay

What was life like for children in the West in the 1800s? Thanks to photography, we can see how they lived, worked, and played. Look at the following pictures to see how their lives were different from yours. In what ways were their lives the same as yours?

Photographer taking picture—early 1900s

Many American Indian people, like this Cheyenne family, moved from camp to camp. They followed the buffalo each year. Babies rode on a cradleboard. Horses carried older children. The lives of these people changed very little for many generations. But by 1855, more and more settlers were moving onto American Indian lands in the West.

Look at the picture. This Cheyenne family is moving. Why do you think they are moving? Why did the lives of the American Indians change?

In 1862, a new law gave more land in the West to settlers. They could have land if they lived on it for five years. Many pioneer families went west in covered wagons. The wagons carried all of their belongings across prairies and mountains. Once pioneers reached their new land, they often lived in their wagons until they could build a house.

How did *pioneer* families travel to the West? Once they got to the West, what did they do?

After 1865, many pioneers set up homesteads in the West. Living on a homestead was hard work. Families had to build houses, plant crops, and raise animals. They often lived far from towns or other houses. They had to rely on themselves. Small children fed chickens and gathered firewood. Older children milked cows, washed clothes, and even hunted.

Describe life on a *homestead*. How was it different from your life?

Some people who had been slaves journeyed west. Thousands of black families left the South. They wanted to buy land and create a new life. Many went to Kansas. There, they started new towns. This family waits for a steamboat in Mississippi around 1880. The boat will take them to St. Louis, and from St. Louis, they will head farther west.

How do you think this family feels about moving west? Why does the family want to go west?

By 1890, most American Indian families had been forced to live on reservations, land set aside for Indian use. Cheyenne families like this one were moved to reservations in Oklahoma and Montana. These people were no longer allowed to follow the buffalo. The tepee and strips of meat drying outdoors shown here were traditional customs. This family also used tin plates and buckets like the pioneers. Even though they had to get used to new ways, they worked hard to keep their traditions.

How did life in the West change for people like this *Cheyenne* family?

By 1900, more towns were growing in the West. Many families did well in their new towns. They created new communities. Children could go to school. They could play with friends who lived nearby. In small towns in Kansas, children from many places went to school together.

Life was an adventure for children in the West in the 1800s, whatever their background.

What was life like in the West for some pioneer families?

Timeline

For each picture, name the year and describe what happened during that time in history.

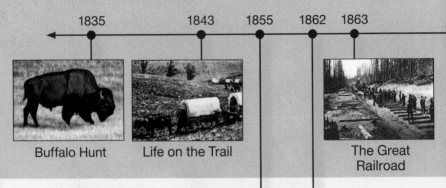

| 1835 | 1843 | 1855 | 1862 | 1863 |

Buffalo Hunt   Life on the Trail   The Great Railroad

Look at this row. For each picture, name the year and then tell what happened during this time in history to the American Indians.

Cheyenne Families
Followed Buffalo

Now look at the last row. Name the year and describe each picture. Explain how life was different for American Indian families compared with pioneer families.

Pioneer Families
Moved West

58

1865   1880   1885   1890   1900

Betsy's
New Home

American Indians
Were Moved to
Reservations

Pioneers
Made Homes

Black Families
Journeyed West

Pioneers Built
Schools and Towns

UNIT 16
Wild, Wild West

The Cowboy Trail

by Roseanne Parry

illustrated by Wilson Ong

Between 1867 and 1880, cowboys herded thousands of cattle to market.

Chapters 1, 2

Vocabulary

★ for·tune

A **fortune** is a very large amount of money.

People hoped to make a *fortune* by moving to the West and finding gold. Complete the sentence: I might make a fortune if I . . .

★ cat·tle drive

When many cattle are herded across miles of land, it is called a **cattle drive**.

During a *cattle drive*, cowboys on horseback drove hundreds of cattle to the railroad stations. The cowboys went on a . . .

★ cour·age

When you have **courage**, you are brave or able to do difficult things.

To keep the baby cow from drowning, the cowboy pulled it out of the rushing water. What did the cowboy show? How?

★ = New

stam·pede

When a group of animals becomes frightened and runs wildly in panic, it is called a **stampede**.

Thunder and lightning scared the horses. When they ran, it was called a . . .

★ pre·vent

Prevent means to stop something from happening.

We wanted to *prevent* a forest fire, so we were careful to put out the campfire. What do traffic signs help prevent?

Idioms and Expressions

★ in spite of

In spite of is another way of saying something didn't stop us.

The cowboys kept the cows moving *in spite of* the storm. Did the storm stop the cowboys? What did they keep doing in spite of the storm?

63

Chapter 1

The Cowboy Life

The West in the 1860s

In the 1860s, the West was a wide-open place. Buffalo, elk, wolves, and coyotes roamed the prairies. Millions of longhorn cattle ran wild along the Rio Grande River.

Cowboys and Cattle Drives

Texans began rounding up their longhorn cattle and driving them north to the railroad. A man could make a fortune selling longhorn cattle to be shipped by train to the city.

Men came from all over to join the cattle drives. These men were called cowboys. Cowboys were black, white, Mexican, and American Indian. There were cowgirls too. On the trail, it didn't matter if you were rich or poor or even a former slave. Strength and courage mattered.

Why did Texans round up longhorn cattle? What two characteristics did a cowboy need to have?

A Cowboy's Job

Cowboys worked from before sunup to long after dark. The trail was hot and dry in the summer. Rattlesnake bites and lightning strikes were common. Cowboys drove cattle to the railroad stations year round. They drove the cattle through hailstorms and even blizzards. Cattle thieves sometimes attacked. One of the most dangerous things was a stampede. In a stampede, the cattle would run wild and trample everything in their path—cactuses, trees, even cowboys.

In spite of the hard work and danger, most cowboys loved their jobs. They told stories and sang songs about the cowboy life. In 20 years, more than a million cattle were moved along the trails.

Why do you think it was important for cowboys to have strength and *courage*? Why do you think cowboys loved their jobs?

The Cattle Drives End

Settlers moved west too. They built farms and fences. Barbed wire fences were invented to prevent cattle from trampling crops. The railroad moved farther and farther west, and by 1900 the long cattle drives were over.

Think and Talk

MAIN IDEA

1. Finish this sentence: In the 1800s, cowboys had to have strength and courage because . . .

DRAWING CONCLUSIONS

2. How did barbed wire fences and the expansion of the railroads end the long cattle drives?

Chapter 2

A Cowboy's Story

I am 17. I am a free man. All my life, my family lived in a one-room shack. My family farmed all day on the same little patch of ground.

One day, I got myself a horse and a broadbrim hat. I left that little patch of land and rode the open range. I moved longhorn cattle up the trail hundreds of miles, from the Rio Grande Valley to the railroad yard in Kansas.

I was a cowboy. We were white, Mexican, Indian, and black, but we all ate together around a campfire. We treated each other with respect. On the trail, the only things that mattered were strength and courage.

Our cook got coffee and bacon ready long before sunup. He cooked us three square meals a day. He could also shoe a horse in 10 minutes flat and set our broken bones. He would stitch a cowboy's sleeve to the chest of his shirt to keep a broken arm steady.

Plenty of danger was waiting along the trail— rattlesnakes, hailstorms, blizzards, and stampedes. Sometimes the cattle got spooked. They would run in all directions. They trampled everything in the way—cactuses, trees, even cowboys.

The cowboy life was hard. But I loved my horse and that wide-open Texas sky. Come night, when the stars were out, I rode around the herd. I sang the folk songs Mama taught me to settle the cattle down for the night. I'd sit up tall and proud in the saddle and say to the stars, "At last! I am a free man!"

Describe the cowboy. Why do you think this cowboy sat tall and proud in the saddle?

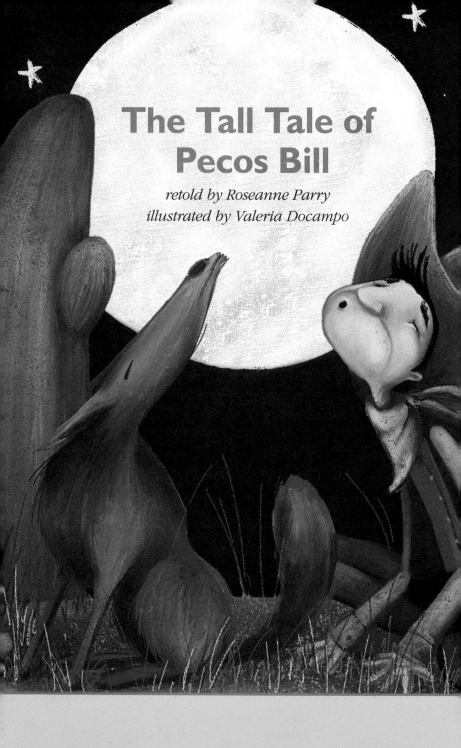

The Tall Tale of Pecos Bill

retold by Roseanne Parry
illustrated by Valeria Docampo

Introduction, Chapters 1, 2

Vocabulary

★ **ex·ag·ger·ate**

Exaggerate means to make something seem bigger, better, worse, or more important than it is.

Zach claimed he caught a giant fish. What did Zach do? How did he *exaggerate*?

★ **i·ma·gi·na·tive**

Something that is **imaginative** has new and interesting ideas.

Dinosaurs Before Dark was an *imaginative* story. Why?

★ **im·pos·si·ble**

Something that is **impossible** can't be done.

It's *impossible* for a pig to fly. What else is impossible?

★ **chal·lenge**

A **challenge** is something that is new or difficult for you.

Riding a wild horse would be a *challenge*, even for an expert rider. Why?

 ★ = **New**

★ **wid·ow**

A **widow** is a woman whose husband has died.

My grandfather died many years ago. My grandmother is a . . .

★ **de·clare**

Declare means to say something very clearly.

The mayor *declared* that the park will be open to everyone. What did the mayor do?

★ **las·so**

Lasso means to catch something using a rope with one end tied in a circle.

The cowboy *lassoed* the cow and brought it back to the ranch. What else could you lasso?

Idioms and Expressions

★ **neck and neck**

When racers are **neck and neck**, they are so close that it is impossible to tell who is ahead.

The two horses raced *neck and neck* all the way to the finish line. Complete this sentence: It was hard to tell who was ahead because the racers were . . .

★ **= New**

Introduction

Stories about Pecos Bill and Slue-Foot Sue are tall tales. The storytellers exaggerated for fun—making characters bigger and stronger than any real person could be. The imaginative events were often impossible.

Tall tales were told as people gathered around a campfire after a hard day's work. These stories helped cowboys and settlers have fun, laugh, and face the challenges of their everyday lives.

Chapter 1

Pecos Bill Becomes a Cowboy

Who is this tall tale about? Listen for *exaggerations* and events that are *impossible*.

When Pecos Bill was a small boy, he bounced out of his family's covered wagon. The Pecos River took him deep into the heart of West Texas. Lucky for Bill, a coyote mother found him and raised him up as her own pup. Bill learned to run, eat, and sing like a coyote.

What did Bill think he was? Why did Bill act like a coyote?

One day, Pecos Bill saw a cowboy filling his canteen at the river. The cowboy greeted Bill. "Howdy, partner. How come you don't have a horse?"

"Coyotes don't ride horses," Bill answered.

"Shucks, you're a man. You aren't a coyote. Where's your tail?" asked the cowboy.

Bill turned around 10 times and didn't see his tail once. "Well, tie me up and call me a gopher," Bill said. "I must be a man after all."

From that day, Bill decided to be a cowboy.

Close your eyes and *imagine* Pecos Bill turning around 10 times looking for his tail. Do you think that's funny? Why or why not? How did Bill find out he was a man?

"If you're going to be a cowboy, you'd better get a horse," the cowboy said.

Bill noticed a silver mustang out in the sagebrush. "I like that one," he said.

"That horse is called Widow Maker because no one can ride him," warned the cowboy. "He eats gunpowder for breakfast and fireworks for lunch."

"That's my kind of horse," Bill said.

Bill let out a yip-yahoo and ran to catch Widow Maker. The silver horse galloped away, faster than the wind. Bill and Widow Maker ran neck and neck across the tall grass prairie. They ran clear to the North Pole and back without breaking a sweat.

Why was the horse called *Widow* Maker? What did the horse eat?

"You are the fastest cowboy in the West," Widow Maker said. "We should be partners."

And from that day on, they were.

Think and Talk

CHARACTERIZATION

1. Describe the main character.

EXPLANATION

2. Explain why Bill thought he was a coyote.

LITERARY ANALYSIS

3. Let's reread the chapter and find the exaggerations and impossible events that make this a tall tale.

Chapter 2

Pecos Bill Rides a Wild Cyclone

What is Bill going to do in this tall tale? Why is that an exaggeration?

One day, Bill rode Widow Maker to the Rio Grande. He saw a gal riding by on a 50-foot catfish, swinging a gator by the tail and shouting yip-yahoo like a coyote. It was Slue-Foot Sue.

Bill's heart melted.

Bill was about to declare his true love to Sue when the sky grew dark. A cyclone spun up. It headed straight for town.

"Excuse me, Miss," Bill said. "Someone has got to explain to that there cyclone that it has no business going into town."

Bill walked up to the cyclone. He grabbed it and tried to wrestle it to the ground, but the twister kept on twisting.

Why did Bill wrestle with the cyclone?

Bill lassoed it. He hopped on its back and steered it out of town. Bill rode that whirlwind 27 hours a day, 17 days a week. He rode it clear across Texas and New Mexico.

In Arizona, Bill put on the brakes. He dug his heels into the dirt. The cyclone dragged Bill along until they carved out the Grand Canyon.

How did Pecos Bill make the Grand Canyon?

Some folks say Bill rode that cyclone clear up to the moon. Other folks say that on a hot Texas night when you hear a yip-yahoo, that's just Pecos Bill having a wild time. And if it suits your fancy, you can yip-yahoo right back.

Think **and Talk**

CHARACTERIZATION

1. Describe what else you learned about the main character.

EXPLANATION

2. What prevented Pecos Bill from telling Sue that she was his true love?

LITERARY ANALYSIS

3. Let's reread the chapter and find the exaggerations and impossible events that make this a tall tale.

The Tall Tale of Slue-Foot Sue

retold by Roseanne Parry
illustrated by Valeria Docampo

Look at the picture. Describe what you see. Where do you think this story takes place?

Chapters 1, 2

Vocabulary

★ **swamp**

A **swamp** is land that is always wet or covered with water. A swamp is also called a slue.

No home could be built on a *swamp*. Why not?

★ **spunk**

Spunk is the courage and energy to do difficult things.

The little girl showed a lot of *spunk* when she competed in the talent contest. Complete this sentence: I show spunk when I . . .

★ **spunk·y**

Spunky describes someone who has the courage and energy to do difficult things.

The *spunky* little girl played basketball with bigger and taller girls. What do you know about the little girl?

★ **= New**

★ lunge

Lunge means to move suddenly toward someone or something, especially to attack them.

The deer *lunged* at each other with their horns. What were they doing?

Now You Try It!

Try defining each word. Then look up the word in the glossary. Your definition might be better!

chal·lenge

Start with "A *challenge* is . . . "
Let's find the word on page 95.

ex·ag·ger·ate

Start with "*Exaggerate* means to . . . "
Let's find the word on page 98.

★ = New

Chapter 1

Slue-Foot Sue in the Swamp

A long time ago in Louisiana lived a gal named Sue. Folks said that she was full of spunk. She wasn't afraid of the darkest night or the wildest weather. She could wrestle a hurricane right back out to sea and let out a holler folks could hear a hundred miles away.

Sue roamed around the swamp in her own boat, pushing it with a long pole. When a gator swam up looking for lunch, she swung him by the tail just to hear his teeth rattle. She spent so much time in the blackwater swamp that folks called her Slue-Foot Sue.

Take a look at the *spunky* girl named Sue. Close your eyes. Imagine Sue standing in her boat swinging an alligator by its tail.

One day, a bear came out of the backwoods. It scared away the fishermen and ate up their fish. It scared away the farmers and ate up their chickens. But that bear did not scare Sue.

"Go away!" Sue shouted from her canoe. The bear stole Sue's lunch pail and ate her jam sandwiches.

"Now you've gone too far," Sue yelled. She whacked the bear with her push pole. The bear snapped it in two with his teeth. He lunged at Sue and wrestled her down into the dark water. She wrestled him right back. They growled and shoved all day and into the night.

What did the bear do to the fishermen and farmers? What made Sue mad at the bear?

"You don't scare me," Sue said. "But I bet I can scare you."

"Scare me? Impossible!" said the bear. "You're just a little gal."

"Sit yourself down, Mr. Bear, but don't get too comfortable."

Sue told that bear a story so scary, so creepy, so full of horrors that the bear's hair stood up. His eyes bugged out. He jumped clean out of his skin and ran away, never to be seen again.

How did Sue scare the bear? Close your eyes. Imagine the bear with its eyes bugged out. Now imagine the bear jumping out of his skin and running away.

Think and Talk

CHARACTERIZATION

1. Describe what you learned about Slue-Foot Sue.

DRAWING CONCLUSIONS

2. How do you think the people in Slue-Foot Sue's community felt about her? Why?

LITERARY ANALYSIS

3. Let's reread the chapter and find the exaggerations and impossible events that make this a tall tale.

Chapter 2

Slue-Foot Sue
Dances Up a Storm

A long time ago, there lived a spunky gal named Sue. Sue lived in the great state of Louisiana.

Sue's mother was an Irish fiddler. She taught Sue to dance an Irish jig so light she was three feet off the ground. Whenever there was a shindig or a hootenanny, Sue was right there dancing the stars clean out of the sky.

What were some of Sue's special talents?

Word got around about the dancing gal named Slue-Foot Sue. A challenge came from Texas—a dance contest.

Sue arrived in style, with one foot on the back of a coyote and the other on a cougar.

The banjo and fiddle players tuned up. The judges swept the barn floor. The dancers laced up their best shoes. Then with a loud yip-yahoo, the music began.

Sue danced a line dance, a square dance, and a round dance with ease. She moved on to the rectangle dance. Other dancers dropped out, gasping for air. The triangle dance finished off the rest of them. Sue was the winner! The crowd went wild, but Sue didn't stop to take a bow.

She went straight into a spin. She spun like a top. The floor started to smoke. Sue spun straight through the floor. She drilled a hundred feet down.

Just when folks thought she might vanish forever, a gusher of oil came out of the hole with Sue riding on top.

Think and Talk

CHARACTERIZATION

1. What was Slue-Foot Sue famous for?

COMPARE AND CONTRAST

2. What was the same about Pecos Bill and Slue-Foot Sue? What was different?

LITERARY ANALYSIS

3. Let's reread the chapter and find the exaggerations and impossible events that make this a tall tale.

Fluency

The Ballad of Pecos Bill and Slue-Foot Sue

by Ann Watanabe

illustrated by Valeria Docampo

Come listen to a story about a boy named Bill.   10

A big, strong baby liked rolling down the hill.   19

One day in a wagon, his family moved away,   28

And Bill bounced out, much to his dismay.   36

In the river, that is, the Pecos River.   44

Well, the next thing you know, the coyotes took Bill.   54

They raised him as their own, oh, what a thrill.   64

One day by the river, Bill met a cowboy.   73

Bill found he had no tail, so he must've been a boy.   85

A boy, that is, a human boy.   92

Well, now it's time to say hello to cowboy Bill. 10

Riding Widow Maker, he never stays still. 17

One day he met a gal named Slue-Foot Sue. 27

Sue melted his heart, and soon they were two. 36

Got married, that is, Pecos Bill and Slue-Foot Sue. 46

Well, that Slue-Foot Sue had a lot of spunk. 10
She rode Widow Maker and was thrown with a clunk. 20
Sue bounced so high, she bounced to the moon. 29
"Ah, oooo," howled Bill. "Bounce back soon." 36

Howling, that is, howling at the moon. 43

To this very day, Bill's never heard from Sue. 52
That poor old Bill is still sad and blue. 61
If you hear a howl late in the night, 70
It's Bill's lonely cry in the pale moonlight. 78

Howling for Sue, that is, Slue-Foot Sue. 86

Glossary

Arapaho

Arapaho is the name of an American Indian tribe.

The *Arapaho* people live in the area now known as the states of Colorado, Wyoming, and Oklahoma.

belongings

Belongings are things that you own. They belong to you.

We packed our *belongings* in suitcases.

cattle drive

When many cattle are herded across miles of land, it is called a **cattle drive**.

During a *cattle drive*, cowboys on horseback drove hundreds of cattle to the railroad stations.

challenge

A **challenge** is something that is new or difficult for you.

Riding a wild horse would be a *challenge*, even for an expert rider.

Cheyenne

Cheyenne is the name of a Great Plains Indian tribe.

In the *Cheyenne* tribe, the women took down the tepees whenever the tribe moved.

communicate

> **Communicate** means to share ideas or feelings with someone else.
>
> Our big smiles *communicate* that we are happy.

community

> A **community** is a group of people or animals that live and work together.
>
> Our school is a *community*.

courage

> When you have **courage**, you are brave or able to do difficult things.
>
> To keep the baby cow from drowning, the cowboy pulled it out of the rushing water. The cowboy showed great *courage* when he saved the baby cow.

dangerous

> When something is **dangerous**, it is not safe.
>
> The sign means something is *dangerous*.

DANGER
DO NOT ENTER
AUTHORIZED
PERSONNEL ONLY

dawdle

> **Dawdle** means to do something slowly.
>
> Sometimes, I *dawdle* on my way to school.

declare

Declare means to say something very clearly.

The mayor *declared* that the park will be open to everyone.

distance

Distance is the amount of space between things. A distance can be very small or very large.

When my friend lived next door, there was very little *distance* between our houses.

dugout

A **dugout** is a room that is made by digging a large hole in the ground or the side of a hill.

Long ago, people sometimes had to live in a room made in the side of a hill. That room was called a . . .

embarrassed

Embarrassed means to be uncomfortable or nervous and worried about something you've done.

Tim was *embarrassed* when he dropped his lunch.

Glossary

exaggerate

Exaggerate means to make something seem bigger, better, worse, or more important than it is.

Zach claimed he caught a giant fish. How did he *exaggerate*?

exhausting

Something that makes you really, really tired is **exhausting**.

Miss Tam's long plane ride to Ghana was *exhausting*.

former

We use the word **former** to describe what someone used to be.

Mrs. Jones is a *former* soldier, but now she's a teacher.

fortune

A **fortune** is a very large amount of money.

People hoped to make a *fortune* by moving to the West and finding gold.

homestead

A **homestead** is a large piece of land given to a settler to farm.

Many settlers started farms on their *homesteads*.

imaginative

Something that is **imaginative** has new and interesting ideas.

Dinosaurs Before Dark was an *imaginative* story.

immigrant

A person who moves from one country to another is called an **immigrant**.

Immigrants came to the United States from many other countries.

impossible

Something that is **impossible** can't be done.

It's *impossible* for a pig to fly.

lasso

Lasso means to catch something using a rope with one end tied in a circle.

The cowboy *lassoed* the cow and brought it back to the ranch.

leggings

Leggings are clothes that cover just your legs or part of your legs.

Dancers often wear *leggings* to keep their legs warm.

Glossary

lunge

Lunge means to move suddenly toward someone or something, especially to attack them.

The deer *lunged* at each other with their horns.

Missouri

Missouri is one of the 50 United States.

Pioneers started their trips to the West in *Missouri*.

pioneer

A **pioneer** is one of the first people to travel to a new place.

The first people who traveled west in covered wagons were called *pioneers*.

prairie

Prairie is flat, open land that is covered with grass.

Much of the middle part of the United States is still *prairie*.

prevent

Prevent means to stop something from happening.

We wanted to *prevent* a forest fire, so we were careful to put out the campfire.

ravenous

When you are **ravenous**, you are very hungry.

I was so ravenous after swimming that I ate four sandwiches.

rely

When you **rely** on someone, you trust and expect help from that person.

Some students rely on the bus driver to get to school each day.

reservation

A **reservation** is an area of land that is set aside for a special purpose.

As settlers built homes in the West, the Indians living there were sent to live on reservations.

scorcher

When a day is very hot, people call it a **scorcher**.

I worked outside in the sun yesterday, and it was quite a scorcher.

scout

On a hunt or expedition, a **scout** will leave the group to go see what is ahead.

When Jack and his friends went exploring, Jack was the scout.

settler

settler is someone who moves to where few people are living and makes a home there.

Settlers moved to the West by wagon train.

spunk

Spunk is the courage and energy to do difficult things.

The little girl showed a lot of *spunk* when she competed in the talent contest.

spunky

Spunky describes someone who has the courage and energy to do difficult things.

The *spunky* little girl played basketball with bigger and taller girls.

stampede

When a group of animals becomes frightened and runs wildly in panic, it is called a **stampede**.

When the horses were scared by the thunder, the cowboy couldn't stop the *stampede*.

swamp

A **swamp** is land that is always wet or covered with water. A swamp is also called a slue.

No home could be built on a *swamp*.

trade

If I give you something, and you give me something in return, we **trade**.

Jose and Trevor liked to *trade* baseball cards.

trader

Someone who trades with another person is called a **trader**.

Trevor and his friends are card *traders*.

tribe

A **tribe** is a group of people who live in an area together. Members of a tribe share the same customs, language, and beliefs.

There are more than 500 American Indian *tribes*.

the West

If you look at a map of the United States, the land on the left side of the Mississippi River is called **the West**.

My family is planning to drive from the Bronx to *the West*.

widow

A **widow** is a woman whose husband has died.

My grandfather died many years ago. My grandmother is a *widow*.

103

Glossary

willow branch

A **willow branch** comes from a willow tree. A willow branch is long and thin and bends easily.

We cooked our hot dogs on *willow branches* over the campfire.

Idioms and Expressions

hold my head up high

When I **hold my head up high**, I am proud of something I did.

I could *hold my head up high* because I did my best.

in spite of

In spite of is another way of saying something didn't stop us.

The cowboys kept the cows moving *in spite of* the storm.

make a name for ourselves

When we **make a name for ourselves**, we do something so great that other people hear about us.

Our baseball team won so many games that we *made a name for ourselves.*

neck and neck

When racers are **neck and neck**, they are so close that it is impossible to tell who is ahead.

The two horses raced *neck and neck* all the way to the finish line.